YOUR FAVOURITE
BEDTIME
STORIES
by Uncle Arthur
3

Illustrations by Annette Agard

ISBN 0-904748-72-3
ISBN 0-904748-75-8 5-volume set

Printed and published by
The Stanborough Press Ltd.
Alma Park, Grantham, Lincs., NG31 9SL
England

CONTENTS

The boy who lost five pounds

'Malcolm,' called Father, who was busily hammering in his workshop. 'Come out here, will you?'

'Yes, Dad,' said a sleepy voice in the dining-room.

'Come on then. I want you to give me a hand.'

'I don't want to come out,' said the voice from indoors. 'It's too cold.'

'Come on, Malcolm. Don't hang about. I'm in a hurry.'

Malcolm thought it was about time to move, and came out of the dining-room.

'What do you want me to do?' he asked, yawning.

'Do?' asked Father. 'There's heaps of things to do. I'm just going to build a new chicken-house at the bottom of the garden, and I want you to help me carry the timber down there.'

'Umph,' growled Malcolm. 'I was just going to have a game . . . '

'This will be a great game,' said Father firmly. 'Come on now, get busy. There's the wood, and you know where to take it.'

'Where shall I take it?' said Malcolm, trying to delay the work as long as possible.

'Down to the bottom of the garden.'

'Which wood do you want me to take?'

'*This wood*,' said Father, getting a little cross. 'All of it.'

'But I can't carry all that.'

'Yes, you can. Hurry up now. I shall be down there with the tools before you.'

Malcolm moved slowly over to the pile of timber.

'Aw, Dad,' he said, 'it's too heavy.'

'Too heavy! What, for a big boy like you?'

'Can't lift it,' said Malcolm.

'Why not?'

'Too heavy.'

Malcolm picked up one plank and let it slip out of his hand with a resounding crash.

'No good,' he said. 'Can't do it.'

'Now look here,' said Father, suddenly getting a bright idea. 'How soon could you get that wood to the bottom of the garden if I were to give you a five pound note?'

'Five pounds?' questioned Malcolm, suddenly forgetting all that he had been saying. 'Five pounds? Would you really give me a five pound note for carrying this down the garden?'

'I didn't promise it,' said Father, 'but I asked how long it would take you to carry this to the bottom of the garden if I gave you five pounds. . . . '

'I don't know,' said Malcolm, a little uncertain as to what Father was getting at.

'Would you like five pounds for doing it?' asked Father.

'You bet I would!' said Malcolm.

'Well,' said Father, 'before we make the arrangement, let me see how fast you would carry it if I did give you five pounds.'

'All right,' said Malcolm, seizing the top piece of timber and dashing off down the garden as fast as his legs would go. In less than two minutes he was back again at the shed.

'Was that fast enough?' he asked.

'Just fantastic!' said Father. 'So the timber wasn't so heavy after all. Now you can go inside.'

'Go inside!' exclaimed Malcolm. 'What for? There's all this wood to carry down the garden.'

'I know,' said Father. 'That's quite all right. I'll carry it down myself.'

'But I want to do it,' said Malcolm. 'I want to earn that five pounds you said I could have.'

'I dare say you do,' said Father, 'but it's too late now.'

'Too late?' said Malcolm. 'There's plenty of time before dark.'

'Oh, I didn't mean that,' said Father, a little sadly. 'I meant that if you had done it for me at first, without all that grumbling and growling, I would gladly have given you five pounds, and even more, for helping me. But if my son won't work with me just for love I certainly don't want him to do it just for money. I'd much rather do it all myself.'

There was an awkward silence, and Malcolm walked back to the house to think it over.

Early next morning, as Father was shaving in the

bathroom, a noise in the back garden caused him to look out of the window. At the bottom of the garden he noticed a strange pile of clean, white timber. Half way up the garden, walking towards the house, was Malcolm, his face radiant at the thought of the great secret he would spring on Father at breakfast time. In a flash Father understood. In another flash he was downstairs, with one side of his face all shaving cream. The next moment he was upstairs in the bathroom again, completing his interrupted shave. But he'd just had time to put something underneath Malcolm's porridge plate. It was the five pound note that had been lost — and won.

Scott against the storm

Scott was 9 years old at the time this happened. Summer months are very hot in the country where he lives. In the July heat wave Scott's father decided to take the family to the seaside for a holiday.

There were five in the family: Daddy, Mummy, Kent, Sonia and Scott. To save money they took their own tent and booked in at a caravan park. There were lots of other campers there, and it promised to be a wonderful time, meeting new friends, paddling and swimming through the long summer days.

Scott helped Daddy put up the tent, while Sonia made a bed for herself in the family car. Then they all went for a swim in the bay.

They enjoyed two wonderful days and nights together. The weather was all they could have hoped for. Then, on the third night, came a change. In no time at all a terrible storm roared in bringing with it thunder, lightning, rain and wind — but as often happens the wind was worst of all.

As the wind howled and the canvas flapped wildly, Scott could hear that the large tent next door had collapsed when its centre pole fell. Another tent had its frame twisted. One corner of Scott's family's tent began to bend, and stayed that way. Scott held on to another

13

corner, trying to keep it steady, but it was more than he could do. He was getting tired and felt he couldn't stand there much longer. That's when he thought of Jesus.

What a wonderful thing that was! Here was a 9-year-old boy trying to hold up a tent pole in a fearful wind, with rain pouring down in torrents, with lightning flashing and thunder roaring — and he thought of Jesus.

It was Scott against the storm all right, but he knew where to turn for help. This is what he had to say:

'I prayed to Jesus to stop the storm. I said, "Jesus, the tent's blowing away. Please stop the storm!" '

Over and over he prayed his prayer while he stood there holding the swaying pole.

Then suddenly there was a great calm. The rain stopped and the wind died down. As the pole ceased swaying, Scott ran outside. The stars were shining. There was hardly a cloud in the night sky. He could hardly believe that a storm could stop so suddenly.

'Thank you, Jesus,' he said.

In the morning Sonia woke up in the car and wondered why everybody was talking about a terrible storm.

'What storm?' she asked. 'I never heard a thing.'

Maybe she didn't. But she missed something. Not the storm, but the way it stopped, and why. Probably Scott is the only one who really knows, and he'll never forget it as long as he lives.

Sad birthday

It was Anne's birthday. She was just 9 years old, and very proud of the fact.

To celebrate the big event she asked her friend Michelle to go with her to the picnic area down by the river. Michelle said she would love to, and when both mothers had agreed, off they went, taking their lunch with them.

It was a glorious day and they had a wonderful time. They roamed all over the place, from the river bank up to the top of the cliffs and back again.

The sunshine, the flowers, the breeze, and the rippling water made them think that heaven itself could hardly be more beautiful.

But just as trouble entered the Garden of Eden, so it came into this little earthly paradise, and in exactly the same way, too, through temptation.

Only here it wasn't a fruit tree that was the cause of it, but a bridge.

Anne and Michelle had looked up at it many times, admiring the beauty of its arch and wishing that they might walk across it some day. Once or twice they had gone close enough to read the notice, 'DANGER: KEEP OFF', and they wondered why there was any danger.

'I can't see why they don't let people walk across,' said Anne. 'After all, only two or three trains go over it all day long. Surely it would be all right to cross it between times.'

'We'd better not,' said Michelle. 'We'd only get into trouble. See the other notice, "TRESPASSERS WILL BE PROSECUTED." I wouldn't want to be prosecuted, whatever that means.'

'That doesn't mean anything,' said Anne. 'They wouldn't prosecute two little girls.'

'I don't know,' said Michelle. 'I wouldn't risk it.'

So they stood there a while, looking across the bridge, reading the notices again, and wondering why grown-ups make so many strange rules.

By and by Anne said, 'Do you know what? I'm going to go across. Seeing it's my birthday I think I should give myself a treat. And I've always wanted to walk across that bridge. It won't take me ten minutes to go over and back. Coming? Nobody will see us.'

'Better not,' said Michelle. 'A train might come. You never know.'

'Oh, don't be a cowardy custard,' said Anne. 'Come on. There won't be any train. And if one did come, we could run ahead of it.'

'All right,' said Michelle. 'If you want to go so badly, I'll go with you.'

So they started out. But if they thought they weren't going to be seen, they were mistaken. Hardly had they gone twenty metres when a woman in the picnic area below called out, 'Better get off there, girls. There's a train due any time now.'

'We'd better go back,' said Michelle.

'No,' said Anne. 'We're all right. We can run faster than one of those old trains any day.'

'Get off that bridge!' called the woman in a voice of command. 'You are in great danger. Get off at once!'

'I'm going back,' cried Michelle, running for safety.

But Anne refused to go back. She had made up her mind that she was going to cross the bridge no matter what anybody said. So she went on.

Again came the warning voice: 'Get off the bridge! Run for your life! A train is coming!'

Anne took no notice. She just walked on.

Then she heard a whistle.

Did it come from a policeman? She turned to look, and there was a train coming straight towards her, only a few hundred metres away.

There was no way back now, so she began to run. But she couldn't run fast enough. The train came nearer and nearer. Now she knew there was only one thing to do — jump.

So she jumped. Down, down, down she went, until she fell with a big splash into the river far below.

People who had been watching dashed into the river and pulled her out. But poor Anne was so badly hurt by her long fall that she had to be taken to hospital. It was a sad, sad ending to what had started out as a very happy birthday.

Giving in to temptation, ignoring clear warnings, brings a lot of trouble — just as it did to Adam and Eve in the long ago.

Rags on the razzle-dazzle

Rags was a wire-haired Terrier with soft hair. You couldn't really say he was a thoroughbred, but what did that matter? All the children loved him, and he knew it. Mother loved him, too, but now and then she wasn't too sure.

One thing she had against him was his habit of getting into the Volvo Estate every time she wanted to take the children to town. Sometimes it just wasn't convenient, and she would put her foot down and say he had to stay at home.

Somehow Rags didn't understand — or did he? Maybe it was because he liked being with children so much. Anyway, at such times he would hide under the second seat of the Volvo and lie there very still until they were halfway to town, then he would bound out of his hiding place as if to say, 'Ha! Ha! You can't send me back now!' Of course, the children all said to Mother, 'He'll have to come with us now, won't he?' And he did.

Well, one day Rags pulled off his little trick once too often. Something in his head told him that the car was about to go to town, so, seeing the door open, he crept into his usual hiding place and made himself as small as possible under the seat.

By and by somebody started the engine, slammed the door, and the Volvo was on its way. Rags stayed very still until he thought it was safe to come out then, about halfway to town, he jumped up on to the seat and found to his surprise that he was all alone with Mother!

Mother was not pleased.

'Rags, you naughty dog!' she said. 'If I weren't in such a hurry I'd stop the car and smack you!'

There was something in Mother's voice that told Rags she would really do that if she had time. He slunk down off the seat and crept into his usual hiding place.

When, some minutes later, he felt the car stop in a car park, Rags thought it might be just as well if he could get as far away as possible from Mother's right hand. So, as Mother opened the door, he slipped around her feet and ran away down the street at full speed.

'Rags!' cried Mother, rushing after him. 'Stop! Come back at once!'

But she might as well have called to the man in the moon. He scampered on and, turning a corner, vanished from sight.

Mother went on looking for him for a long time, but finally she gave up and returned to the car. Of course, she really did love Rags and she knew how badly the children would feel if she were to return home without him.

But that is what she had to do, and you can imagine what happened then.

21

All the children were terribly upset and the younger ones cried. Prayers were said for Rags at least three times a day and sometimes, it would seem, every hour. But nothing happened. Rags did not return.

Mother put an advertisement in the local paper. Finally she pleaded with the local radio announcer to say that five little children were praying for their precious Rags to come home.

'Poor Rags!' wailed the children. 'He must be starving by now.'

As a matter of fact he wasn't. Quite the opposite. He was having the time of his life. He was really on the 'razzle-dazzle', living it up as he had never done before.

Rags discovered that the way to get a good meal was to go to a house that had one or two children, then stand outside the back door, whimpering softly and looking just as sad as he could, with his tail between his legs. That was good for one bone and maybe even a whole dish of dog food. It never failed. Instead of having only one meal a day he had five or six, and was on his way to getting very, very fat.

After three days he came to a home where there were several children. When they found him whimpering at the door they took pity on him and let him in. Then they fed him a big bowl of soup which he lapped up as though he hadn't had a bite for a week.

'Poor little dog!' they said. 'He must be lost. Look how hungry he is! Mum, let's keep him!'

Their mother said she'd think about it and ask their

father when he came home from work. But their daddy said a big NO! He had too many mouths to feed as it was, he said. They must take the dog to the kennels; that's where all stray dogs should go.

At that moment the eldest child turned on the radio, just in time to hear the announcer say, 'A wire-haired Terrier has run away from home. He answers to the name of Rags. Five children want him back so much they are praying for him every hour of the day. If you happen to see Rags, please ring 536 7897.'

Daddy grabbed the phone. After dialling the number and waiting he said, 'I think we've got Rags for you.'

Shrieks of joy came from the other end of the line.

Cries of 'Rags is found! Rags is found!' filled the house.

A moment later the Volvo was on its way once more and Rags was brought home in triumph, this time *on* the seat, not *under* it.

Mother didn't smack him after all. She was as happy as the children to have him back.

As for Rags, well, he promised the best he could, with his sad eyes, his floppy ears, and his wagging tail, that he would never go on the razzle-dazzle again.

That's our house!

Sometimes people in big cities find it very hard to get a place to live in. There is such overcrowding, rents are so high and houses are so expensive. Often families have nowhere to go. That's how it was for a lady in London many years ago.

It happened soon after World War II. There was a great shortage of houses at that time. Many had been bombed in the War and very few had been built to replace them.

So great was the shortage that she and her family had to live in a tent. That must have been hard for them, with no proper beds, no furniture to speak of, and no running water.

When the London City Council finally began to build houses, Mother went to the office time and time again to ask when she was going to get one. Always the answer was the same, 'We have your name on the list, but we're giving the houses to the most needy first.'

Mother thought *hers* was the most needy case, but the council did not. So she waited and waited and waited.

Many times she and her eldest daughter, Susan, went out to the place where the new council houses were being built and tried to imagine that one of them was theirs.

Then one day when they were walking around the

new streets Susan said, 'The trouble with us, Mum, is that we don't pray hard enough. We don't really believe that Jesus is going to give us a new house.'

Mother smiled. 'I wish I could believe like that,' she said, 'but we've waited more than two years now and I've about lost heart.'

'You mustn't do that,' said Susan. Then she pointed to the frame of a house that had just gone up.

'See those foundations?' she said. 'Do you think the house they're building there will have a good view?'

'Oh yes,' said Mother. 'I'd love to live in that house when it's finished.'

'So would I,' said Susan. 'What's the number on that notice board?'

'It's number 365,' said Mother. 'Why?'

'Remember it,' said Susan, 'because that's where we're going to live.'

Mother laughed out loud. 'What a girl you are!' she said. 'Such a dreamer of dreams. Whatever makes you think we shall ever live there?'

'I know,' Susan said with quiet confidence. 'Because Jesus just told me. That's our house.'

'That's a lovely idea,' smiled Mother, 'but, well, don't you think we'd better go now — back to our lovely tent?'

So back they went.

Week after week more houses went up and people moved into them — always the more needy ones, as the lady at the council offices said.

Meanwhile, Mother and Susan waited and waited.

Then one day, when they had almost given up hope, a letter arrived from the council offices. 'We are glad to tell you that there is a home available for you at last,' it said.

'Oh, thank God,' cried Mother, bursting into tears.

'But which one?' asked Susan, grabbing the letter. 'Which one?'

'I didn't notice,' said Mother. 'Let's look again.'

Susan saw it first.

It was number 365.

Why Brenda won

When Brenda's parents died in a car crash she was sent to a children's home because there was no one else to look after her.

At first she was very sad because she kept thinking of her mother and father and her old familiar home. The people in charge tried their best to comfort her, but it was no use. She simply could not get over her tragic loss.

Fortunately this children's home was located in a very lovely spot, right beside a beautiful sandy beach. The children could play in the sand, or paddle in the sea, almost any time they wanted to. Yet even this meant nothing to poor, sad little Brenda.

Then one day the house mother told the children that there was going to be a big competition on the beach. There would be prizes for the winners, and some of the important people in the town would be the judges.

'What do we have to do?' asked one of the children.

'That's what I was just going to tell you,' said House Mother.

'First of all, you have to pick a Bible text — a short one — but the one you like the best. Then you write this neatly in the sand and decorate it with shells, flowers or anything else you can find. The judges will decide which are the three best and these will receive first, second and third prizes.'

'Where do we go to do this?' asked Brenda, showing the first sign of interest in something that was going on.

'On the beach, of course,' said House Mother. 'I'll choose the best piece of sand I can find and then you'll all stand in a row. You'll have just two hours to finish your work.'

When House Mother sat down, the girls all began talking about which text they were going to choose and how they planned to decorate it. But Brenda didn't say a word. If she chose a text, that was her secret; so was the way she was going to display it.

Soon the big day came and the children, all very excited, lined up along the beach, each with a small spade in their hand. Already people were gathering, and some of the judges arrived early. They wanted to see the children at work as well as the finished product.

As House Mother shouted, 'Start!' the children got down on their knees and began to work in the sand, talking happily to each other and comparing each other's handiwork.

Not so with Brenda. She was at the end of the line and went quietly on with her work without saying a word to anybody. She worked with speed and skill as though she had done something like this many times before.

First she made a big bank of sand with her spade. Then she cut her text into it: 'God is Love.' The lettering was perfect. After that she ran down the beach to gather shells to ornament it, and finished it off by planting

around it wild flowers that she found on the sand dunes.

'Time!' called House Mother. The girls all stood to attention as the judges walked down the line. The ladies paid nice compliments to everybody, but when they arrived at Brenda's entry it was different.

'This is the work of an artist!' said one. 'I've never seen anything so beautiful.'

'My father was an artist,' said Brenda.

'That helps to explain it,' said the lady. 'Of course, this gets first prize. Don't you agree?' she asked the other judges.

'Yes, of course, of course,' they nodded.

Brenda gave them a shy smile, the first one she'd given anybody since she'd come to the children's home.

Naturally she was happy that her precious text, 'God is Love,' had won first prize. But what pleased her most was the fact that she had done this for her parents.

Pit ponies, Ronnie and heaven

Ronnie loved to go to Uncle Willie's shop. It was the most interesting place in the world. Uncle Willie mended shoes, repaired school bags, and sewed cases. The little boy liked the smell of the leather, and the whirring of the heavy-duty machines was music to his ears.

Best of all, Ronnie liked going to Uncle Willie's because there he heard the most wonderful stories. Every visit was an exciting adventure. Ronnie would live in a world of delight as Uncle Willie told tales of long ago.

On one of Ronnie's visits Uncle seemed to be in a serious mood. He and Ronnie began talking about leaving this old world and going to heaven.

'I can't imagine what heaven will be like,' said Ronnie.

'Ah,' said Uncle Willie, 'there I can help you. I can show you just what it will be like.'

'Show me?' asked Ronnie.

'You'll see,' replied his uncle. 'This very week I'll show you what heaven will be like. Be here at ten o'clock tomorrow morning.'

'Do I have to wait until then? Can't you show me now?'

'No,' said Uncle Willie firmly. 'Tomorrow at ten o'clock; not a moment before.'

Ronnie couldn't sleep that night. 'How can Uncle Willie know what heaven is like?' he asked himself. 'But he's very wise. He must have a really good answer.'

At last it was morning. Ronnie ate hurriedly and dressed and rushed off to his uncle's. When he got there Uncle Willie was ready to go and was starting up his car.

Quickly Ronnie got in, and off they drove, way out into the country — *to a coal mine!*

'Why is Uncle Willie taking me to a dirty old place like this?' Ronnie wondered.

They climbed out of the car, and soon they heard a clattering as the lift came up from the depths of the mine. Quickly, a miner opened a large gate, and out of the lift came six dirty, dazzled pit ponies.

Ronnie couldn't believe his eyes as he saw these creatures stagger out, heads bowed against the bright sunlight. After pulling coal trucks in the dark pit they couldn't see in the brilliance of the daylight and groped around, unsteady and unsure.

Swiftly men took hold of their harnesses and gently led the ponies over the rough surface, away from the mine to the green fields beyond.

'Come on,' said Uncle Willie to Ronnie, 'you still haven't seen heaven. We'll come back later.'

In a couple of days Uncle Willie and the boy were back at the field. What a difference now in the ponies! No longer were their coats dusty and dirty. No longer

were their heads bowed, and no longer did they stagger around.

Now their eyes were adjusted to the brilliant sunlight, and their legs were strong and firm. With manes flying and hooves kicking, they cantered madly through the cool grass, breathing in the precious fresh air. Every step was one of freedom and delight.

'That', said Uncle Willie, 'is heaven! The heaven those ponies know is freedom from darkness, dirt and dust. It's just the same for us, you know. One day we're going to leave this old world, full of darkness, sorrow and sin, and we'll be free to enjoy the pure pleasures of heaven. Just like the ponies, we live in the sunlight of God's love.'

'I want to be there in God's heaven,' resolved Ronnie.

Mike's big bass drum

Mike was a little boy with a lot of aunties.

Too many aunties *he* thought.

He had heard of little boys and girls in mission lands who didn't have nearly enough of anything — and he wondered if they would mind if he sent them some of his aunties. But his dad said that that would not do.

Mike had so many aunties that two of them had the same name. Elsie.

Now when you have two Aunty Elsies how do you tell the difference?

Easy. One of them was long and thin. The other was short and, well, quite fat really. Because of this Mike talked about 'Aunt Elsie' and 'Fat Aunt Elsie'. Fat Aunt Elsie knew this and didn't mind. Like a lot of fat people she was also jolly. Mike's dad used to say: 'Elsie really knows how to have a good time. And when she's having a good time, there's an awful lot of her to have a good time.'

There was another good thing about Fat Aunt Elsie. She only came once a year. Mike thought that this was very civil of her. Most of his aunties visited a little too often and believed it their duty to make sure that Mike had his shoes, nose, knees and neck clean, and his hair tidy — at all times. To Mike this didn't seem very friendly.

Fat Aunt Elsie's week's holiday was in the springtime.

She came when May was out on the hedges and the air was full of exciting smells. Mike and his dad would set out for the railway station. Out from the train would step Fat Aunt Elsie. Dancing round and round, waving her battered brown suitcase in the air she would shriek, 'Well, I'll put to sea in a tub!' and people would hear her for miles around.

Aunty's holiday week was one of the noisiest in Mike's home in the whole year. In Mike's mind the reason this aunty made more noise than all the others put together was mixed up with the fact that she belonged to the Salvation Army. But he didn't mind the noise a bit. In fact, he helped her to make it!

In the Salvation Army, he learned, there was a lot of trumpet-blowing, tambourine-bashing, poem-reciting, song-singing — and banging of the big bass drum.

Aunt Elsie told Mike all about the Salvation Army and even taught him some of the songs. But all that impressed him was how the man with the big bass drum always marched ahead of the band.

He decided that *he* wanted a big bass drum.

One day he went for a walk with his aunt in the countryside. The sun shone, the birds and Fat Aunt Elsie sang and there was much talk of big bass drums. When they left the fields and re-entered the town Mike carefully guided his aunt to a shop window where a toy drum, with two drum sticks, was on display. It was not exactly a *big bass drum*, but Mike knew that it was the nearest he would get to one. And he could tell, just by looking at it, that he could use it to make an awful lot of noise.

For some reason Fat Aunt Elsie didn't really want to buy it for Mike. It took him a long time to talk her into it. But buy it she did.

When Aunt and nephew and the little bass drum entered the little house where Mike lived, his mum fixed the drum with a stare that showed that she was not well pleased.

Mike lost no time before he was getting some practice in.

Dad looked angry and big sister made unkind remarks.

For most of the afternoon Mike marched up and down the long garden, the drum hung round his neck, bashing away for all he was worth, and pretending he was the leader of the band.

Suddenly Mike heard a little piping voice from beyond the high hedge shouting angrily. Looking up, he saw old Miss Clare from next door standing on top of a step ladder, her face purple with rage.

Miss Clare, it appeared, had in one afternoon heard enough of drums to last a lifetime.

Mike ran indoors and told what had happened.

Gently, but firmly, Mum removed the drum to a safe place. Quietly she explained to Mike that it was always good to consider the feelings of others, that hardly anyone liked noise as much as he did, that elderly people especially like peace and quietness — and that,

taking everything into consideration, it might be best if Mike did the generous thing and sold the drum, giving the money to the poor children in mission lands.

Mike was tempted to be sad, but he looked at Fat Aunt Elsie who grinned and said as she so often did: 'Well, I'll go to sea in a tub!'

From slavery to fame

It is hard to realize that slavery was ended not much more than 150 years ago. But it's true. And in the United States there are many people alive today whose grandparents, or great grandparents, were slaves.

Born about 1856, a slave boy named Booker lived in a small log cabin. There was no glass in the windows and the door was too small for the hole in which it swung on rusty hinges. The cabin had no floor save the earth, and the 'store cupboard' for sweet potatoes was a deep hole in the living room, covered with boards. There was also a 'cat hole' in one of the walls about seven inches square, to let the cat pass in and out during the night. But as there were lots of other holes in the shack, Booker thought this one seemed unnecessary.

As a little boy he never played. He didn't know what it was to play. He was always cleaning up, running errands, taking water to the men in the fields. And if he didn't do things exactly right, he was cuffed and beaten by those in charge.

Booker was about 7 years old when freedom came, following the American Civil War. He remembers going to the 'Big House' — as the white people's mansion was called — and hearing somebody read a paper to all the black people who had gathered there. He didn't understand what it was all about but Mother did, and she kept weeping and saying, 'This is the day I have been praying for, but fearing I would never see.'

Free at last, his mother left the plantation and walked over the mountains into West Virginia and settled in a village called Malden. But freedom did not solve all the problems. To Booker it meant working in a salt furnace from four in the morning until late in the afternoon.

He was not able to go to school. There were no schools for black boys and girls in the USA in those days. So he could not read or write. But he did notice that the boss of the packers would put number '18' on the barrels of salt which his stepfather filled, and after a while he was able to draw that figure, though he didn't know about any others.

One day there came into his heart a desire to read, and he begged his mother to get him a book. Somehow, though very poor, she managed to buy one. And what do you suppose it was? A children's story book with pretty pictures? No; an old, worn copy of Webster's spelling book!

At this time, remember, Booker could not read; and there was no one to teach him to read. There was not a single black person anywhere near who could read, and he was too afraid of the white people to ask any of them to help him. So all alone he taught himself the alphabet. After a few weeks he found himself reading that spelling book.

About that time another boy — also black — who had learned to read in a northern state, arrived in the village. As soon as the people found out this boy could read, they arranged to buy a newspaper so that he could read the news to them in the evenings. Booker envied him. He wanted to be able to read like that, too.

Not long after this, a little school was started, the first for black people in all West Virginia. It had only one teacher, and the black people had to pay her themselves. But everybody wanted to go to it — boys and girls, fathers and mothers, even grandfathers and grandmothers. The old people wanted to learn to read the Bible before they died.

Poor little Booker, however, was not allowed to go. His stepfather said he must stay at work and earn money. So he laboured in the salt furnace and watched the other boys and girls going to school.

By much pleading he finally persuaded his stepfather to let him attend school. But it was on the condition that Booker worked from four in the morning till nine, and returned after school for two more hours of work. Booker was so keen to learn, that he was prepared to fall in with his stepfather's plans.

Arriving at school, he ran into a serious problem. When asked for his name, he replied, 'Booker.'

'Booker what?' asked the teacher.

Booker was puzzled. He had only one name, so far as he knew. He had never heard of another. However, if he was supposed to have two, he would invent one. So, 'Booker Washington', he said. And the name stuck to him from then till now. He added the letter T in

between these two names later on. It stands for Taliaferro, a name his mother liked.

Little by little Booker began to learn. Gradually the ambition grew in his heart to get an education and do something worthwhile with his life. Then his step-father made him leave school and go to work in a coal mine. It was a bitter disappointment to the boy, for he hated to work underground. It was so dark down there. Sometimes his light would go out and he would lose himself in the many low, narrow passages. Sometimes there would be explosions and other boys like himself would be hurt.

Yet it was in this very mine that the idea came to him which altered his whole life. One day he overheard two men talking about a great school for black people which had opened somewhere in Virginia. He crept nearer so that he could listen better. The men were speaking of the Hampton Normal and Agricultural Institute, and what they said sounded like heaven to Booker T. Washington. He made up his mind that one day he would go there at all costs.

Two years passed, during which he saved every penny he could for the long journey to Hampton. Yet his wages were so little that in two years he did not have nearly enough to travel the 500 miles to the Institute. But he set off at last, going first in the stage coach, then begging rides in wagons, and walking when he couldn't ride. When he reached Richmond, eighty-two miles from Hampton, his little store of money had run out.

He had nothing left for food. That night, and several nights after, he slept under the wooden pavement of the city streets. Fortunately he was able to get a job at the docks. Here he earned enough to buy food and save a little for the last part of his journey.

After his long journey, and having had no bath or change of clothes for a long time, he was so untidy that the head teacher did not want to let him stay. Several hours passed, and he began to wonder if, after coming so far and putting up with so much, he would have to go back, rejected. Then the lady said to him, 'The next room needs cleaning. Take a brush and sweep it.'

This was his chance. He swept that room three times. He took a cloth and dusted it four times. Every bench, table and desk, all the woodwork around the walls, he dusted again and again till he could find not a speck more to remove. Then he reported to the lady, and she came to inspect what he had done. She looked carefully at everything, even wiping a handkerchief over the table to see if she could pick up any dirt. But there was none. 'I guess you will do,' she said.

This 'entrance examination', Booker said afterwards, was the most important one he ever took.

Now he was in a real school at last! True, he had to work very hard, for he had to earn all his board, room, and tuition expense. But he made the most of every precious hour that he had for study.

Some things, of course, were new and difficult for him. But he learned many things. Most important was the 'dignity of labour', as he afterwards called it — the lesson that to work hard is no disgrace to any boy, but a blessing. Then, too, he learned that life's greatest joys are to be found in helping others. And it was this which led him to give his life to help the less fortunate of his own race. After graduating, in 1875, he went back to his own home village as a teacher. But not long afterwards he was invited to join the staff of the Hampton Institute, where he had been a student.

When a call came for a principal for a new training school at Tuskegee, Alabama, Booker was recommended. Arriving there he asked for the school, but was told, 'There isn't any, yet.'

Undismayed, he replied, 'Then we'll build one.'

This he did, beginning with a small, leaky building with only thirty pupils, and expanding it until it became known as one of the greatest institutions of its kind in the world.

Impressed with the good work Booker was doing for black people in the south, many people, rich and poor, sent him money. Andrew Carnegie gave him $600,000 at one time, while an elderly black lady, over 70 years of age, clad in rags, came to him one day and said, 'Mr. Washington, . . . I know you are trying to make life better for the people of the black race. I do not have any money, but I want you to take these six eggs I have been saving up. . . .' Booker never was quite sure who gave the most, this old woman or Carnegie.

Within a few years Tuskegee had 2,000 students, 133 buildings and 3,550 acres of campus.

When Harvard University awarded Booker T. Washington a degree, its president called him 'a wise helper of his race, a good servant of God and his country'.

Saved from the flood

Night had fallen. Everybody in the little town was asleep. Everybody, that is, except the policeman who was keeping his lonely watch in the police station.

Nobody dreamed that danger was near. No serious trouble had come to the town for years and years. There was no sign of trouble now, except that the level of the water in the river was a little higher than usual. But there, the water often went up like this and down again without anybody noticing it. Sometimes, especially in the hot, dry summer, the river was just a little trickle, way down at the bottom of its forty-foot banks.

The night wore on. There was no sound save the beating of the rain on the roofs and roadways, and the occasional barking of a dog.

Suddenly the telephone rang in the police station.

'Flood warning!' said a voice. 'Lots of water rushing your way. Will reach you in thirty minutes. Get the people out of all houses on low-lying ground. Hurry!'

A flood! In thirty minutes! How little time to warn everybody.

The policeman sounded the alarm. In an instant the whole town was alive. A few minutes later men were hurrying to the houses down by the river, waking the sleeping families and helping them move what they could of their goods to higher ground.

Some of the people, just roused from sleep, didn't

want to move, especially in the middle of the night and with rain teeming down. They couldn't believe that a flood was only a few minutes away. But the policemen and the firemen and other friends hurried them out to safety.

Then it came. About one o'clock in the morning a wall of water, full of uprooted trees, broken houses, and dead animals rushed by. On its churning surface were tables, chairs, oil drums, and cars! It hit the bridge in the middle of the town and carried it away as though it had been paper. It overflowed its banks and filled all the low-lying land nearby. Some of the houses which people had left a few minutes before were lifted off their foundations and sent sailing downstream. Others collapsed and fell apart.

By this time hundreds of people were standing on the high ground near the river peering through the darkness at the terrible scene before them. How glad they were that nobody was in those houses that were being smashed and carried away by the flood!

Nobody?

'Look!' cried somebody. 'Surely that was a light! Over there, look!'

'It can't be,' said the others. 'There's nobody there; and there's no light, anyway.'

'But there it is again! Look! It must be a candle. Somebody keeps lighting it and it blows out.'

'So it is! You're right! Whose house is it?'

'That's Mrs. Smith's house. Her husband's in the

army. She has four little children with her. Didn't anybody warn them?'

'No. Nobody did.' Somehow, in the darkness and the excitement, that house had been missed. Now it was surrounded by wild, rushing water which threatened any moment to carry it away.

'Give me a rope!' cried some brave man. 'I'll swim there!'

They tied a rope round the man and he set off. But he couldn't get anywhere near. It was impossible. The swift current carried him away and it was only with great difficulty that he was hauled back. Another man then another, offered to go, but it was no use. All failed.

Meanwhile, out there in the darkness, a brave little mother was making a gallant fight for life and for the lives of her children.

As no one had called to warn her of the coming flood, she and her children were all fast asleep when the first rush of water came sweeping into the house. Awakened by the shouts of the people looking on, and the roar of the flood waters going by, she had jumped out of bed to find herself standing in two feet of water, which covered the bedroom floor and was fast rising. Suddenly realizing what had happened she grabbed her four children and lifted them one by one on to the top of a large cupboard. Then as the water rose above the beds, the table, and the chairs, she clambered up on top of the cupboard herself, taking with her a candle and matches, a dry blanket, a bottle of milk, a knife, an old chisel, and, of all things, an iron!

Now they were all huddled together on top of the cupboard wondering just how high the water would rise. Then it was that this dear, brave mother began to pray that God would spare her and her children.

An hour passed. Two hours. It was now three o'clock in the morning. They could feel the water close to the top of the cupboard. Suddenly one of the inside walls of the house gave way and fell with a great splash.

'The end must be near, now,' this brave mother said to herself. But she was not ready to give in yet.

Now it was that she made use of the tools she had so wisely brought with her, thinking that she might need them.

Just over their heads was the ceiling made of thin board. 'If I could just cut through it,' she said to herself, we could climb on to the rafters. Then we would be another two feet above the water.'

Seizing the iron and the blunt chisel, she began chipping away at the board, splitting it off in little pieces until she made a hole two feet long and nine inches wide. Through this tiny hole she pushed her children, one by one, telling each to sit on a rafter. She was afraid they might fall through the frail board if they were to stand on it. Then she pulled herself up through the hole and sat with them there waiting, wondering, praying, while the water swirled through the house below.

Four o'clock. Five o'clock. Six o'clock. It was getting light now. And what a scene! The great brown torrent was surging by, with bits of broken houses and furniture floating on its surface. Hundreds of people who had watched all night were looking anxiously at the one little house still standing in the midst of the flood. Only its roof could be seen now, and the tops of some of its windows. Surely everybody in it must have drowned long ago!

But no! Look! Somebody was cutting a hole in the roof!

The brave mother was making her last attempt to save her children. She was going to lift them out on to the roof if need be!

A shout went up from the people and tears came to many eyes.

'Let me try again,' said a strong swimmer. 'I think I can make it now.'

They tied a rope round his waist and he set off through the raging waters. He was swept downstream, but fought his way up again. At last, after a mighty effort, he reached the house.

Tying the rope securely, he made his way in through the window. The large cupboard on which the family had waited so long, and by which they had climbed into the loft, had gone. He signalled back for a ladder. Soon another swimmer, aided by the rope, was on his way with one. Another swimmer followed. Soon one of them was seen coming through the house with a little girl on his shoulder. Then another and another as one by one the children were brought by strong hands along the rope, strained to the uttermost by the fury of the torrent.

Then, as all brave captains are the last to leave their sinking ships, so this dear mother was the last to leave her falling house. When all her four children had been taken to safety she came out herself and, with the help of her rescuers, made her way to land.

What a cheer they gave for her! And she deserved it. I hope her children never forget how they were saved from death that dreadful night. It was a mother's faith against a flood. And it won.

Not for me!

Tim was for ever talking about his 'secret'. Before school, in school, after school, he would whisper in Mark's ear that he had something in his pocket that would really get him excited if he could only see it.

At first Mark took no notice. For one thing he had never liked Tim very much, and for another, he didn't believe that Tim really had any 'secret' at all. But the more Mark tried to leave Tim alone, the more Tim kept talking about his 'secret' and pointing mysteriously to his pocket.

One afternoon during class, when the teacher's back was turned, Tim leaned over and whispered in Mark's ear. It was the same old story, except that this time he said, 'Come with me behind the hedge on the way home. I'll really show you something.'

This was repeated many times as the teacher continued to write on the board. At last Mark began to think that perhaps, after all, he would do what Tim wanted. His curiosity was aroused. What could it be that Tim had to show him that was so very wonderful? Why did it have to be shown in secret, where nobody else could see?

So, at the end of school, Mark followed Tim down the path, wondering what he was going to see. When they had gone some distance Tim suddenly jumped behind the hedge. He called for Mark to follow. Mark stopped.

'Now I'll show you,' said Tim. 'But it's a secret, just between you and me.'

'What is it?' said Mark. 'It must be something very wonderful to call for all this secrecy.'

Slowly and mysteriously Tim put his hand in his pocket and pulled out — a cigarette!

'Yuk!' cried Mark. 'So *that's* the wonderful secret! Just a dirty old cigarette.'

'It isn't dirty and it isn't old,' said Tim. 'What's more, there is something wonderful about this one. The man who gave it to me said so. He said that if you smoke it you will have marvellous dreams.'

'Now look here, Tim,' said Mark. 'I don't know what's happened to you, but let me tell you right now that I'm not interested in your secret. It's just a big fake.'

'Oh, come on,' wheedled Tim, seeming to take no notice of what Mark had said. 'I've got two of them here. One for me and one for you.'

'One for me!' snorted Mark. 'What makes you think I'd want one? Not for me! I don't smoke and I don't want to smoke. Smoking is a filthy habit, and nobody can do his best in life if he uses tobacco or marijuana. They're full of poisons. So you can keep your old cigarettes — or better still, throw them away.'

'Oh, Mark,' coaxed Tim. 'It can't be as bad as that. And think of those dreams.'